Penguin Readers

LITTLE WOMEN

LOUISA MAY ALCOTT

LEVEL

RETOLD BY KAREN KOVACS
ILLUSTRATED BY ALEX OXTON
SERIES EDITOR: SORREL PITTS

PENGUIN BOOKS

UK | USA | Canada | Ireland | Australia
India | New Zealand | South Africa

Penguin Books is part of the Penguin Random House group of companies
whose addresses can be found at global.penguinrandomhouse.com.
www.penguin.co.uk www.puffin.co.uk www.ladybird.co.uk

Penguin Readers edition of *Little Women* published by Penguin Books Ltd, 2020

005

Original text written by Louisa May Alcott
Text for Penguin Readers edition adapted by Karen Kovacs
Text for Penguin Readers edition copyright © Penguin Books Ltd, 2020
Illustrated by Alex Oxton
Illustrations copyright © Penguin Books Ltd, 2020
Cover illustration by Harriet Russell

Printed and bound in Great Britain by Clays Ltd, Elcograf S.p.A.

The authorized representative in the EEA is Penguin Random House Ireland,
Morrison Chambers, 32 Nassau Street, Dublin D02 YH68.

A CIP catalogue record for this book is available from the British Library

ISBN: 978-0-241-39769-5

All correspondence to:
Penguin Books
Penguin Random House Children's
One Embassy Gardens, 8 Viaduct Gardens
London SW11 7BW

Contents

People in the story

Meg (age 16)

Jo (age 15)

Beth (age 13)

Amy (age 12)

Marmee (Mother)

Laurie

New words

Europe

letter

poor

present

rich

war

Note about the story

Louisa May Alcott (1832–1888) lived near Boston, USA. She had three sisters, and her family did not have a lot of money. But Alcott worked, and the money helped her family. In the 1800s, many people were very poor. Often, they did not have money for food or clothes.

Little Women starts in the American Civil War (1861–1865). A civil war is a war between different people in the same country. Alcott could not go to war, because she was a woman, but she worked in a war hospital. At that time, women could not do many things. Women had to have a husband and children — this was very important.

Before-reading questions

1 What do you know about American women in the 1800s? Make sentences with *could* and *could not*.

   They could write books, but they could not go to war.

2 *Little Women* is about a family. Who are the people in your family? How important is family to you?

3 The women in this story do not have a lot of money. How important is money? Can you be happy with no money?

4 Look at the front cover of the book, and read the back cover. What happens in this story, do you think?

5 Look at the "People in the story" on page 4. Talk about them.

   Marmee is the Little Women's mother. She looks happy. I think she is about forty years old.

*Definitions of words in **bold** can be found in the glossary on pages 63–64.

December 1862

I **hate** being poor.

Christmas with no **presents*** is not Christmas!

Some girls have lots of beautiful things, but we have nothing!

We're **lucky** — we've got Father and Mother.

Marmee, is that letter from Father?

Yes, Meg.

He writes: *"I think of the girls every day and night. They must be good. Then, I can be* **proud** *of my little women."*

A happy Christmas

The Laurence boy

I'm a girl. I can't talk to those boys, but I want to.

Oh, sorry!

Don't go, Miss March. I only came here because I don't know many people.

I must say sorry to Jo. Maybe she can forgive me.

Skate here. It's **dangerous** there.

Amy didn't hear Laurie. But I'm angry with her! She can skate in that dangerous place!

CHAPTER FOUR

Dark days

December 1863

We must write to Marmee.

Yes, she must come home.

The next week

Mother!

Where's Mr. Brooke?

He stayed with Father. How's Beth?

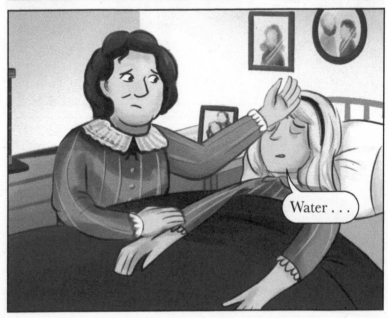

Water . . .

The first wedding

I'm stupid. The food was a lot of money, but only one friend came.

That's sad for you.

Send the food to the poor family. I don't want it.

CHAPTER SIX

Only friends

Summer 1868

I love you, Meg's little babies! But I'm going.

Goodbye, Amy. Enjoy Europe with Aunt Carrol.

Goodbye, Father! Goodbye, Laurie!

Hello, Jo!

...Jo?

Beth can talk to you. I have lots to do.

Marmee, I think Laurie loves me. But to me, he's only a friend. I must go to New York—I can be a tutor there. Then, he can forget me.

Yes.

Listen—it's a letter from Jo. *"To Marmee and Beth. I like it in New York. I have a friend here. He's called Mr. Bhaer. He's a German teacher. In the evenings, he teaches me . . ."*

CHAPTER SEVEN

Europe

Spring 1870

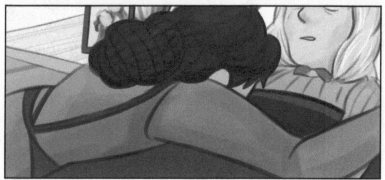

November 1870

Laurie, you're home. Where's Amy?

My wife is at Meg's house.

Your *wife*? Oh, I'm happy!

I loved you, Jo, but I was a boy. I'm a man now.

The next day

"... You miss Beth a lot, I know. You must write stories—you enjoy that. Your friend, Mr. Bhaer."

December 1870

Oh, Mr. Bhaer!

CHAPTER EIGHT
A happy family

Spring 1872

Aunt March died yesterday.

That's sad.

She gave me her house. She loved me, but I didn't know.

You can have that big house?

Now I can open a school for little boys with no mothers. I can be their mother, and Mr. Bhaer can be their teacher.

Jo, you're very good!

And Laurie, I'm proud of you. You're not lazy now. You work hard, and you help poor people with your money. You're a good person!

Thank you, March family! You gave me love. I'm lucky.

Families are a beautiful thing!

Fall 1877

During-reading questions

Write the answers to these questions in your notebook.

CHAPTER ONE

1 Why is the March family poor?
2 Does Jo like being a girl? Why/Why not?
3 Who wrote the letter? Where is that person?

CHAPTER TWO

1 What do the girls get for Christmas?
2 Where do the March family take their Christmas breakfast? Why do they do this?
3 What does Jo do to Meg's hair?

CHAPTER THREE

1 Who do Jo and Meg meet at the party? Is he rich or poor?
2 Who is Mr. Brooke?
3 Jo, Laurie, and Amy go skating. Why does Jo say sorry to Amy on page 25?

CHAPTER FOUR

1 What is Jo's new job?
2 Jo gives Mrs. March some money. How did she get the money?
3 Why does Mrs. March come home?

CHAPTER FIVE

1 Aunt March is not happy at the wedding. Why not?
2 Why does Amy say "I'm stupid" on page 35?
3 Mr. Brooke gets a new coat. How?

CHAPTER SIX

1 Which sister goes to Europe?
2 Why does Jo go to New York?
3 Where is Laurie going?

CHAPTER SEVEN

1 Which sister dies?
2 Which sister is Laurie's wife?
3 Jo and Mr. Bhaer's wedding must wait. Why?

CHAPTER EIGHT

1 Jo has a big house. How did she get it?
2 Why is Jo proud of Laurie?
3 What job does Jo do now? What does Mr. Bhaer do now?

After-reading questions

1 Do you like the people in this story? Complete these sentences.
   I like ... because ...
   I do not like ... because ...
2 Does Jo have a good life at the end of the story? Does Amy have a good life? And Meg? Why?
3 The sisters try to be better (see page 12). Do you think they are good people at the start of the book? Are they better at the end? How?
4 Why does Meg marry Mr. Brooke? Why does Amy marry Laurie? Why does Jo marry Mr. Bhaer?
5 Is Mrs. March a good mother? Why/Why not?

Exercises

1 **Match the words to the pictures in your notebook.**

Example: 1—c

1 rich
2 war
3 present
4 poor
5 letter

a   b   c   d   e

2 **Write the correct names in your notebook. Use one name twice.**

| Amy | Meg | Jo | Beth |

1 *Amy* is selfish.
2 .... is often angry.
3 .... is vain.
4 .... is shy.
5 .... hates being a girl.

3 **Complete these sentences in your notebook, using *like* or *does not like* + *-ing*. Use the words from the box to help you.**

| be poor | work for Aunt March | go to school |
| be a girl | play the piano | |

1 Amy *does not like being poor*
2 Jo ....
3 Amy ....
4 Beth ....
5 Jo ....

CHAPTER THREE

4 Complete these sentences in your notebook, using the words from the box.

tutor	carriage	burned	skating
	hurt	forgive	

1 "I have a ....*tutor*.... His name is Mr. Brooke."

2 "My foot is .... I can't walk home."

3 "I can take you home in my grandfather's ...."

4 "I was angry, and I .... your story."

5 "I'm going .... with Laurie."

6 "I must say sorry to Jo. Maybe she can .... me."

CHAPTER FOUR

5 Correct these sentences in your notebook.

1 Amy wrote a short story for a newspaper.
   Jo wrote a short story for a newspaper.

2 Mrs. March gets a letter. "Your husband is coming home," it says.

3 Laurie goes with Mrs. March to see Mr. March.

4 Jo sells a story and gives the money to Mrs. March.

5 Beth is ill, and she does not get better.

6 Mrs. March comes home with Mr. Brooke.

7 Mr. Brooke says to Amy, "Please be my wife."

8 Jo does not like weddings, because she wants a husband.

CHAPTER FIVE

6 Complete these sentences in your notebook, using the words from the box.

too	only	some

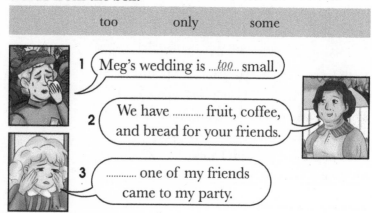

1 Meg's wedding is ...*too*... small.

2 We have .... fruit, coffee, and bread for your friends.

3 .... one of my friends came to my party.

CHAPTER SIX

7 Write the correct answers in your notebook.

1 Meg has a **baby** / *two babies*.

2 Beth loves **Laurie** / **is ill**.

3 Jo is **at war** / **teaching in New York**.

4 Jo **wants** / **does not want** a husband.

CHAPTER SEVEN

8 Are these sentences *true* or *false*? Write the correct answers in your notebook.

1 Amy and Laurie are in Europe in winter 1869. *true*

2 Amy thinks Laurie is lazy.

3 Amy dies.

4 Jo loves Mr. Bhaer.

5 Mr. Bhaer is rich.

9 Complete these sentences in your notebook, using the prepositions from the box.

in	at	for	of	to	at	with	of

1 ...*In*.... spring 1872, Aunt March dies.
2 Jo opens a school .... boys .... no mothers.
3 Jo is proud .... Laurie.
4 .... the end .... the book, the family is .... Jo's house.
5 Jo says thank you .... her mother.

10 Complete these sentences about the seasons in the USA in your notebook. Use the words from the box.

winter	summer	spring	fall

1 In ...*winter*..., you can go skating.
2 In ...., apples are ready to eat.
3 In ...., it is hot.
4 In ...., it is warm, and you can see lots of flowers again.

11 Choose the correct answers for questions 1–3. Then match the characters with their other names (questions 4–6).

1 You use **Miss / Mrs. / Mr.** for a woman with no husband.
2 You use **Miss / Mrs. / Mr.** for a woman with a husband.
3 You use **Miss / Mrs. / Mr.** for a man.
4 Jo   **a** Mr. Brooke
5 John   **b** Mrs. March
6 Marmee   **c** Miss March/Mrs. Bhaer

Project work

1   You are Jo. Write one page of her diary in 1862
    (Chapter One). Then, write one page of her diary in 1877
    (Chapter Eight). What is she doing? What does she want?
    Is she happy?

2   Make a presentation about *one* of these things:
    Feminism
    Louisa May Alcott wrote *Little Women*. She was a feminist.
    * What is a *feminist*? Look online, and find the answer.
    * Which person, or people, in the book are feminists?
      How do you know?
    * Do you think *Little Women* is a feminist book? Why?
    * Are *you* a feminist? (Men can also be feminists.)
    * Do you know any famous feminists who live now?
    OR
    The American Civil War (1861–1865)
    Little Women starts in the Civil War. Find the answers to these
    questions.
    * What does *civil war* mean?
    * Who was the US President at the time?
    * Who was at war? Why were they at war?
    * How many people died in the war?
    * Who won the war?
    * Talk about your country. *My country had a civil war in . . .*

An answer key for all questions and exercises can be found at
www.penguinreaders.co.uk

Glossary

aunt (n.)
the sister of your mother
or father

burn (v.)
to make fire

carriage (n.)
People sit in a *carriage*, and a
horse pulls it.

coat (n.)
You wear a *coat* over your
clothes in cold weather.

dangerous (adj.)
You can have an accident in
a *dangerous* place.

end (n.)
A story finishes at the *end*.

forgive (v.)
Someone does something bad
to you, and you are angry.
Then, after some time, you are
not angry with them. You
forgive them.

grandfather (n.)
the father of your mother
or father

hate (v.)
You *hate* a thing because you
do not like it.

hurt (adj.)
You have an accident, and then
you are *hurt*.

ill (adj.)
An *ill* person is not very well.

invitation (n.)
You ask someone to come to
your party. This is an *invitation*.

kind (adj.)
A *kind* person wants to help
other people.

laugh at (phr. v.)
Bad people *laugh* at you, and
then you are sad. They are
not *kind*.

lazy (adj.)
Lazy people and animals do not
like working hard.

lose (v.)
past simple: **lost**
You had something before, but
you do not have it now. You *lost*
that thing.

lucky (adj.)
Good things happen to a *lucky* person.

miss (v.)
You *miss* someone. You are sad because they are not with you.

newspaper (n.)
You read about the news or stories in a *newspaper*. You can work for a *newspaper* as a job.

piano (n.)
You play music on a *piano*. It has black and white keys (= you put your fingers on these).

present (n.)
We give people *presents* at Christmas.

proud of (adj.)
You work hard. You are a good student. Your parents are *proud of* you.

selfish (adj.)
A *selfish* person does not think about other people.

sell (v.)
past simple: **sold**
Someone gives you money for a thing. You *sell* it to them.

shy (adj.)
A *shy* person does not like talking to new people.

skate (v.)
to move around on ice (= very cold, hard water) in shoes made for ice.

theater (n.)
You go to a *theater* to watch a play (= people showing a story).

tutor (n.)
A *tutor* teaches students at home.

vain (adj.)
Vain people think they are very beautiful.

wedding (n.)
Two people marry at a *wedding*.